LEVEL 1 For first readers

* short, straightforward sentences
* basic, fun vocabulary
* simple, easy-to-follow stories of up to 100 words
* large print and easy-to-read design

LEVEL 2 For developing readers

* longer sentences
* simple vocabulary, introducing new words
* longer stories of up to 200 words
* bold design, to capture readers' interest

LEVEL 3 For more confident readers

* longer sentences with varied structure
* wider vocabulary
* high-interest stories of up to 300 words
* smaller print for experienced readers

LEVEL 4 For able readers

* longer sentences with complex structure
* rich, exciting vocabulary
* complex stories of up to 400 words
* emphasis on text more than illustrations

Make Reading Fun!

Once you have read the story, you will find some amazing activities at the back of the book! There are Excellent Exercises for you to complete, plus a super Picture Dictionary.

But first it is time for the story . . .

Ready?
Steady?
Let's read!

Tim Warnes

Can't You Sleep, Dotty?

LITTLE TIGER PRESS
London

Dotty could not sleep.

Tick-Tock!
Tick-Tock!

So she started to howl.

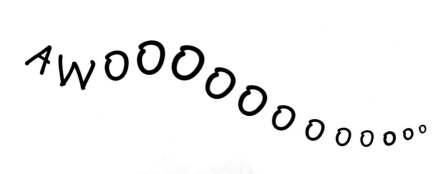

"Try counting the stars," said Pip.

But Dotty could only count to one.

"Have a little drink,"
said Susie.

So Dotty had
a little drink.

Slurp!
Slurp!

But then she made a puddle.

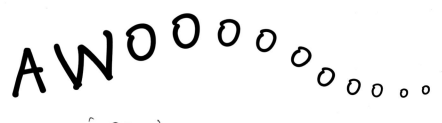

"I hide in my burrow at bedtime," said Whiskers.

So Dotty dived under
her blanket.

But it was too dark.

"I like to sleep where it is sunny," said Tommy.

Plod
Plod

Dotty liked that idea . . .

. . . so she turned on her torch!

"Turn it off, Dotty!" shouted her friends.

Yikes!

Poor Dotty. Then Tommy
had an idea. All Dotty
needed was . . .

. . . a cuddle!
    Night night, Dotty.

Excellent Exercises

Have you read the story? Well done! Now it is time for more fun!

Here are some questions about the story. Ask an adult to listen to your answers, and help if you get stuck.

Sleepy Dog

Dotty cannot get to sleep! What do *you* do to help you fall asleep?

Top Toys

Can you name Dotty's toys in this picture? What toys do *you* like to take to bed?

Pip's Plan

Now describe what Dotty is doing in this picture.

Night Night!

Can you remember how Dotty falls asleep at the end of the story?

Picture Dictionary

Can you read all of these words from the story?

blanket

cuddle

howl

night

puddle

sleep

stars

torch

under

whiskers

Can you think of any other words that describe these pictures – for example, what colours can you see? Why not try to spell some of these words? Ask an adult to help!

Linda Jennings   Basia Bogdanowicz

Make reading fun with amazing activities!

Fred

Fred has a new little door. It's called a cat flap. But Fred knows that Horrible Henry is waiting outside, ready to pounce . . . !

My Turn!

When Oscar and Tilly go to the playground, they are not keen to wait their turn. Will the two friends find a way to play together?

David Bedford
Elaine Field

Make reading fun with amazing activities!